Carol Vorderman

Maths ✓
Made Easy
ExtraTests

Author and consultant Sean McArdle

Key Stage 2
AGES
8-9

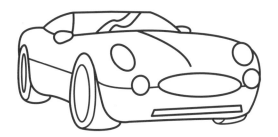

LONDON, NEW YORK, MUNICH, MELBOURNE, and DELHI

DK UK
Senior Editor Deborah Lock
Art Director Martin Wilson
Publishing Director Sophie Mitchell
Pre-production Francesca Wardell
Jacket Designer Martin Wilson
Maths Consultant Sean McArdle

DK Delhi
Editorial Monica Saigal, Tanya Desai
Design Pallavi Narain, Dheeraj Arora,
Tanvi Nathyal, Jyotsna Khosla
DTP Designer Anita Yadav

First published in Great Britain by
Dorling Kindersley Limited
80 Strand, London, WC2R 0RL

Copyright © 2013 Dorling Kindersley Limited
A Penguin Company

10 9 8 7 6 5 4 3 2 1
001—187385—July/2013

A CIP catalogue record for this book
is available from the British Library
ISBN: 978-1-4093-2365-5

Printed and bound in China by L. Rex Printing Co., Ltd.

All images © Dorling Kindersley
For further information see: www.dkimages.com

Discover more at
www.dk.com

Contents

This chart lists all the topics in the book. Once you have completed each page, stick a star in the correct box below.

These are large numbers, so be careful how you read and write them.

Write the number in words.

6 124   Six thousand, one hundred and twenty four

5 102   Five thousand, one hundred and two

7 034   Seven thousand, and thirty four

11 638   eleven thousand, six hundred and thirty eight

17 400   Seventeen thousand, and four hundred

20 805   twenty thousand, eight hundred and five

23 967   twenty three thousand, nine hundred and sixty seven

97 452   ninty seven thousand, four hundred and two

Write the number.

One thousand and forty nine   1 049

Two thousand, nine hundred and eighty four   2,984

Three thousand, four hundred and seventeen   3,417

Six thousand, four hundred and seventy six   6,476

Thirteen thousand, one hundred and six   13,106

Twenty-three thousand and ninety seven   23,097

Sixty thousand and twenty four   60,024

Fifty-four thousand and three   54,003

Completing sequences ★

Complete each sequence.

Some answers have negative values.

12	24	36	48	60	72	34	46
24	32	40	48	56	44	52	66
18	27	36	45	54	63	72	81
45	50	55	60	65	70	75	80
−40	−35	−30	−25	−20	15	10	5
−18	−15	−12	−9	−6	−3	0	3
−36	−32	−28	−24	−20	18	19	10
−70	−60	−50	−40	−30	20	20	0
63	52	41	30	19	8		
80	71	62	53	44			
26	21	16	11	6			
−8	−12	−16	−20	−24			
13	26	39	52	65			
−31	−25	−19	−13	−7			
12	18	24	30	36			

Complete this sequence but be careful because this is a bit trickier.

2	4	8	16			

Try to answer these questions as quickly as possible – but still be correct!

3 x 10 = 30   7 x 10 = 70   9 x 10 = 90   10 x 10 = 100

12 x 10 = 220   0 x 10 = 10   14 x 10 = 790   1 x 10 = 10

15 x 10 = 250   17 x 10 = 770   21 x 10 = 210   30 x 10 = 30

10 x 2 = 20   10 x 6 = 60   10 x 0 = 10   10 x 8 = 80

10 x 13 = 130   10 x 24 = 240   10 x 50 = 550   10 x 22 = 220

10 x 15 = 250   10 x 36 = 360   10 x 100 = 100   10 x 6 = 60

2 x 100 = 200   4 x 100 = 400   6 x 100 = 600   11 x 100 = 178

0 x 100 = 100   5 x 100 = 500   14 x 100 = 224   15 x 100 = 115

1 x 100 = 100   7 x 100 = 700   9 x 100 = 900   19 x 100 = 219

100 x 8 = 800   100 x 14 = 114   100 x 3 = 300   100 x 10 = 100

100 x 18 = 118   100 x 23 = 46   100 x 61 = 61   100 x 32 = 332

100 x 0 = 0   100 x 55 = 155   100 x 82 = 782   100 x 16 = 116

$\frac{1}{2}$ x 10 = 20 $1\frac{1}{2}$ x 10 = 120   100 x $\frac{1}{2}$ = 200 $2\frac{1}{2}$ x 100 = 222

Dividing by 10 and 100 ★

Divide each number by 10.

20 [2]   50 [5]   90 [9]   10 [1]   100 [10]

30 [3]   60 [6]   70 [7]   80 [8]   40 [4]

Write the answers.

60 ÷ 10 = [6]   80 ÷ 10 = [8]   10 ÷ 10 = [1]   40 ÷ 10 = [4]

70 ÷ 10 = [7]   20 ÷ 10 = [2]   90 ÷ 10 = [9]   50 ÷ 10 = [5]

Divide each amount by 10.

120 p [20p]   170 mm [70]   200 g [2]   90 p [9]

250 mm [250mm]   400 kg [4]   110 cm [10]   30 l [30]

50 km [5km]   180 m [80]   500 kg [5]   230 g [30]

Write the answers.

140 kg ÷ 10 = [40]   70 p ÷ 10 = [7]   80 g ÷ 10 = [8]

280 m ÷ 10 = [80]   330 p ÷ 10 = [30]   560 m ÷ 10 = [80]

400 kg ÷ 10 = [4]   780 g ÷ 10 = [80]   20 l ÷ 10 = [20]

Divide each number by 100.

400 [4]   600 [6]   800 [8]   100 [1]

Write the answers.

4 500 ÷ 100 = [5]   2 800 ÷ 100 = [8]   6 400 ÷ 100 = [4]

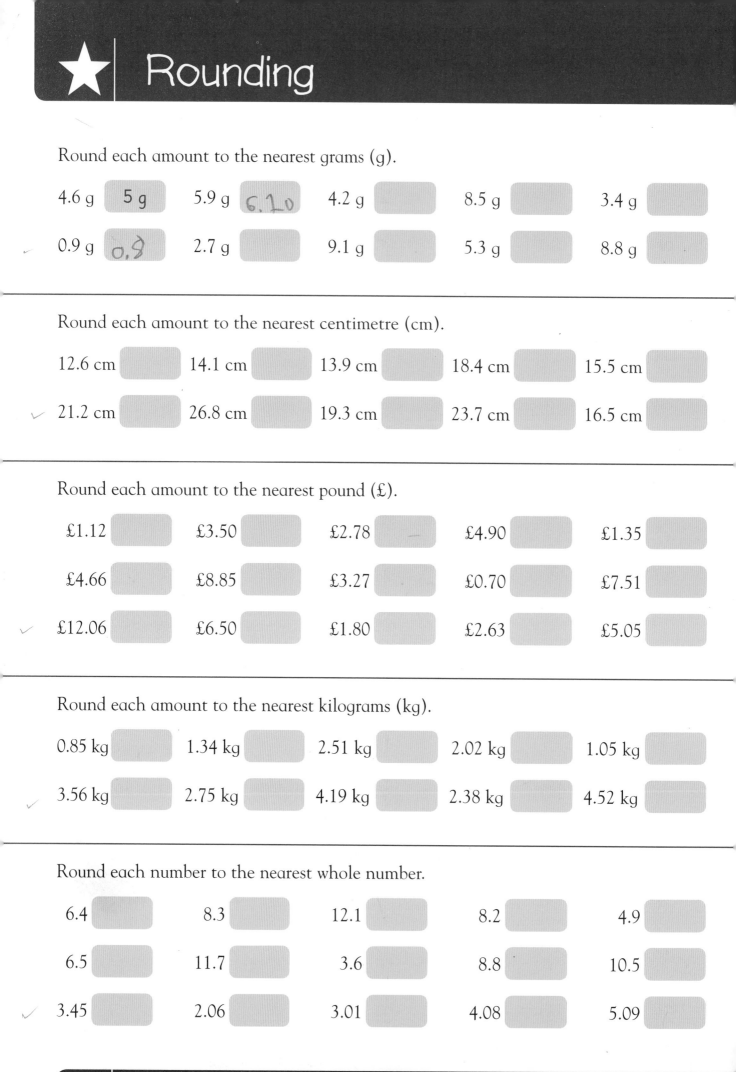

★ Rounding

Round each amount to the nearest grams (g).

4.6 g `5 g`   5.9 g `6.20`   4.2 g ____   8.5 g ____   3.4 g ____

0.9 g `0.9`   2.7 g ____   9.1 g ____   5.3 g ____   8.8 g ____

Round each amount to the nearest centimetre (cm).

12.6 cm ____   14.1 cm ____   13.9 cm ____   18.4 cm ____   15.5 cm ____

21.2 cm ____   26.8 cm ____   19.3 cm ____   23.7 cm ____   16.5 cm ____

Round each amount to the nearest pound (£).

£1.12 ____   £3.50 ____   £2.78 ____   £4.90 ____   £1.35 ____

£4.66 ____   £8.85 ____   £3.27 ____   £0.70 ____   £7.51 ____

£12.06 ____   £6.50 ____   £1.80 ____   £2.63 ____   £5.05 ____

Round each amount to the nearest kilograms (kg).

0.85 kg ____   1.34 kg ____   2.51 kg ____   2.02 kg ____   1.05 kg ____

3.56 kg ____   2.75 kg ____   4.19 kg ____   2.38 kg ____   4.52 kg ____

Round each number to the nearest whole number.

6.4 ____   8.3 ____   12.1 ____   8.2 ____   4.9 ____

6.5 ____   11.7 ____   3.6 ____   8.8 ____   10.5 ____

3.45 ____   2.06 ____   3.01 ____   4.08 ____   5.09 ____

Circle the larger number or amount each time.

(0.5) or 0.3   0.5 kg or 600 g   ½ or 0.3

1.2 or (2.1)   70 cm or (0.5 m)   (£2.40) or 189 p

(5.6 m) or 600 cm   0.3 or (0.4)   £1.90 or (£5.00)

Circle the smaller number or amount each time.

0.8 or (½)   3.5 m or (290 mm)   4.2 or (2.4)

(3.5) or 5.3   (625 cm) or 6.2 m   (130 g) or 1.2 kg

3.5 l or (3 ⅓ l)   £3.50 or (250 p)   (65 cm) or 1 m

Circle the larger number or amount each time.

(6 x 7) or 40   (2 x 12) or 22   (double 150) or 295

(3.5 km) or half of 5 km   (3 x 8) or 6 x 3   (£2.50) or 300 p

400 ml or (0.5 l)   (40 x 2) or 10 x 7   (4 m) or 54 cm

Circle the smaller number or amount each time.

6 kg or (53 g)   6.72 or (6.27)   £7.00 or (1000 p)

12 km or (half of 14 km)   (4.01) or 4.1   2 km or (1 600 m)

2.65 km or (2.56 km)   (4.2 g) or 0.5 kg   (3.6 m) or 400 cm

Circle the larger number each time.

10 x 11 or (12 x 10)   (8 x 7) or 6 x 9   (7 x 4) or 6 x 5

(4 x 11) or 6 x 7   6 x 4 or (9 x 3)   11 x 3 or (9 x 8)

(5 x 8) or 7 x 5   (6 x 6) or 8 x 4   (10 x 5) or 5 x 5

★ Fractions

What is half ($\frac{1}{2}$) of each amount?

£3.00 **£1.50**   £5.00 3,000   6 kg 3 kg   3 g 2g   60 m 6m

£1.20 1,70   £1.50 £1.30   12 ml 6 ml   £2.50 2.30g   6 m 3 m

What is two-thirds ($\frac{2}{3}$) of each amount?

12 m 0   21 kg 20   15 g 10   £6.00 3.00   30 m 20m

18 g 16   £3.00 3.00   21 km 25   24 kg 20 kg   15 m 70

What is a quarter ($\frac{1}{4}$) of each amount?

£1.00 0   60 cm 30   2 m 1   48 g 24   £4.00 £2.00

120 cm 70   80 g 00   12 kg 6   32 p 20   56 g 33

What is one-fifth ($\frac{1}{5}$) of each amount?

20 p 10   50 p 30p   10 p 5   25 cm 13   £20.00 £10.00

60 cm 300h   10 m 5 m   40 km 20km   35 g 20   45 kg 22kg

What is two-fifths ($\frac{2}{5}$) of each amount?

30 p 20p   £20.00 20.00   10 cm 5   5 m 3   2 m 2

40 p 30   50 g 40   60 kg 30   55 p 50   25 p 12

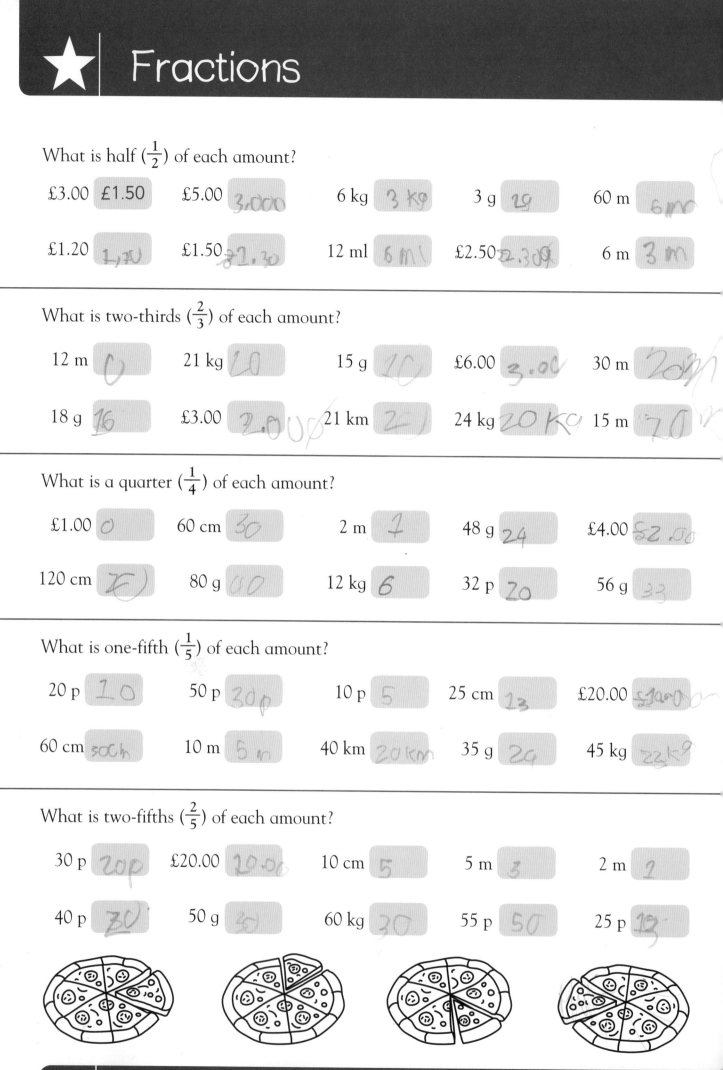

Fractions and decimals ★

Write each fraction as a decimal.

$\frac{1}{2}$ [0.5] $\frac{1}{4}$ [2·4] $\frac{1}{10}$ [2·70] $\frac{2}{10}$ [ ]

$\frac{3}{10}$ [3·10] $\frac{4}{10}$ [4·10] $\frac{1}{5}$ [2·5] $\frac{24}{100}$ [ ]

$\frac{5}{10}$ [5·20] $\frac{15}{100}$ [15·500] $\frac{6}{10}$ [6·70] $\frac{35}{100}$ [ ]

$\frac{7}{10}$ [7·10] $\frac{8}{10}$ [8·70] $\frac{50}{100}$ [ ] $\frac{9}{10}$ [ ]

Write each decimal as a fraction in its simplest form.

0.2 $\frac{2}{2}$ 0.4 $\frac{2}{4}$ 0.6 $\frac{2}{6}$ 0.8 $\frac{2}{8}$

0.5 $\frac{1}{9}$ 0.7 $\frac{2}{4}$ 0.25 $\frac{15}{25}$ 0.75 $\frac{2}{25}$

0.1 $\frac{1}{1}$ 0.3 $\frac{1}{3}$ 0.9 $\frac{9}{9}$ 0.15 $\frac{1}{25}$

How many tenths are equivalent to $\frac{20}{100}$?   [$\frac{200}{70}$]

How many hundredths are equivalent to $\frac{6}{10}$?   [$\frac{600}{70}$]

Which of these is the same as 20 305? Circle the correct answer.

Twenty thousand, three hundred and fifty   Twenty-three thousand and five

Twenty thousand, three hundred and five   Twenty thousand and thirty five

Complete each sequence.

18	14	22	20	24	22	20	−10
−14	−9	4	2	6	72	70	21
12	10	8	6	4	2	0	−2

Write the answers.

45	100	100	78
x 10	x 27	x 0.5	x 100
450	2 700	005	2 800

Find the answer to each problem.

$+\begin{array}{r}16\\12\\\hline 28\end{array}$

The temperature at the South Pole is −16°C and during a storm goes down by another 12°C. What is the temperature during the storm?

−28°C

$\begin{array}{r}^4\\ -5\,{}^1 1\\ 2\;5\\\hline 2\;6\end{array}$

$+\begin{array}{r}£36\\£15\\\hline 51\end{array}$

Peter has £36 and is given another £15 but then goes to the shops and spends £25. How much does Peter have left after his visit to the shop?

£26

Place the amounts in order, starting with the smallest.

| £6.50 | 560 p | £6.05 | £65.00 | 680 p | £5.06 |
| £5.06 | 560P | £6.05 | £6.50 | 680P | £65.00 |

These are some of the ingredients for a cake.

Round each amount to the nearest 10 g.

6 g of salt .....10.g.....

122 g of flour .....120 g.....

67 g of cherries .....70 g.....

45 g of almonds .....50 g.....

A class usually has 33 children but two-thirds
are away on a trip.
How many children did not go on the trip?

30

How many tenths are equivalent to one half?

5

How many thirds are equivalent to one whole?

6

How many quarters are equivalent to 2?

7

Write each decimal as a fraction.

0.5 $\frac{10}{2}$ 0.2 $\frac{2}{10}$ 0.75 $\frac{3}{4}$ 0.9 ———

Write each fraction as a decimal.

$\frac{4}{10}$ 4.20 $\frac{7}{10}$ 2.20 $\frac{37}{100}$ 37.200 $\frac{12}{100}$ 12.200

★ Adding

Write the answers.

46 + 20 = 66   21 + 30 = 51   54 + 40 = 94   53 + 10 = 63

73 + 30 = 103   69 + 40 = 109   45 + 70 = 115   95 + 20 = 115

67 + 50 = 117   70 + 60 = 130   90 + 90 = 180   40 + 80 = 120

49 + 13 = 62   52 + 18 = 70   62 + 12 = 74   37 + 16 = 53

46 + 32 = 78   53 + 27 = 80   38 + 43 = 81   74 + 17 = 91

76 + 28 = 104   44 + 66 = 110   12 + 73 = 85   55 + 23 = 78

Write the answers.

```
  73      56      39      52      51
+ 15    + 17    + 24    + 38    + 26
  88      73      63      00      77
```

```
  25      67      48      90      85
+ 45    + 44    + 28    + 23    + 17
  70     111      76     113     102
```

Write the answers.

£8 + £80 + £4 =

60 cm + 6 cm + 12 cm =

32 cm + 64 cm + 8 cm =

21 cm + 20 cm + 19 cm =

£45 + £25 + £15 =

12 p + 24 p + 36 p =

35 p + 45 p + 16 p =

12 p + 13 p + 14 p =

Write the answers.

40 − 12 = 28   50 − 17 =   60 − 11 =   80 − 19 =

90 − 18 =   30 − 10 =   100 − 15 =   60 − 45 =

26 − 14 =   39 − 16 =   42 − 11 =   63 − 22 =

76 − 34 =   96 − 45 =   54 − 40 =   59 − 28 =

46 − 17 =   52 − 16 =   73 − 19 =   25 − 17 =

34 − 18 =   48 − 29 =   40 − 26 =   81 − 44 =

Write the answers.

$$\begin{array}{r} 35 \\ -12 \\ \hline \end{array} \qquad \begin{array}{r} 41 \\ -20 \\ \hline \end{array} \qquad \begin{array}{r} 57 \\ -25 \\ \hline \end{array} \qquad \begin{array}{r} 63 \\ -41 \\ \hline \end{array} \qquad \begin{array}{r} 44 \\ -34 \\ \hline \end{array}$$

$$\begin{array}{r} 27 \\ -19 \\ \hline \end{array} \qquad \begin{array}{r} 32 \\ -14 \\ \hline \end{array} \qquad \begin{array}{r} 54 \\ -26 \\ \hline \end{array} \qquad \begin{array}{r} 70 \\ -37 \\ \hline \end{array} \qquad \begin{array}{r} 36 \\ -17 \\ \hline \end{array}$$

Write the answers.

47 cm − 34 cm =   59 p − 28 p =   70 m − 32 m =

£40 − £26 =   61 p − 34 p =   73 cm − 48 cm =

64 m − 49 m =   53 p − 49 p =   25 p − 24 p =

21 p − 17 p =   41 p − 38 p =   £98 − £45 =

Write the answers.

35 x 3 = 105   42 x 3 = ⬚   38 x 5 = ⬚   74 x 3 = ⬚

69 x 2 = ⬚   71 x 3 = ⬚   56 x 4 = ⬚   73 x 3 = ⬚

67 x 4 = ⬚   58 x 2 = ⬚   14 x 6 = ⬚   23 x 6 = ⬚

44 x 3 = ⬚   52 x 6 = ⬚   46 x 3 = ⬚   32 x 4 = ⬚

Write the answers.

29	36	45	54	62
x 3	x 4	x 5	x 6	x 7
87	144	225	324	434
2	2	2	2	1

71	86	93	73	64
x 4	x 3	x 4	x 5	x 2
284	258	372	365	128
	1	1	1	

59	43	23	38	40
x 4	x 5	x 6	x 4	x 6
236	215	138	152	240
3	1	1	3	

56	63	76	41	67
x 3	x 4	x 2	x 5	x 7
168	252	152	205	469
1	1	1		4

78	89	37	48	59
x 8	x 10	x 5	x 6	x 7
624	890	185	288	413
6		3	4	6

Dividing with remainders ★

Write the answers. Some of these answers may have remainders.

$27 \div 4 =$ 6 r3 $\qquad$ $24 \div 4 =$ 6 $\qquad$ $47 \div 4 =$ 11r3 $\qquad$ $44 \div 4 =$ 11

$29 \div 3 =$ 9r2 $\qquad$ $14 \div 3 =$ 4r2 $\qquad$ $17 \div 3 =$ 5r2 $\qquad$ $21 \div 3 =$ 7

$12 \div 7 =$ 1r5 $\qquad$ $56 \div 7 =$ 8 $\qquad$ $77 \div 7 =$ 11 $\qquad$ $23 \div 7 =$ 3r2

$15 \div 5 =$ 3 $\qquad$ $6 \div 5 =$ 1r1 $\qquad$ $12 \div 5 =$ 2r2 $\qquad$ $34 \div 5 =$ 6r4

$10 \div 8 =$ 1r2 $\qquad$ $57 \div 8 =$ 7r1 $\qquad$ $84 \div 8 =$ 10r4 $\qquad$ $24 \div 8 =$ 3

$48 \div 6 =$ 8 $\qquad$ $38 \div 6 =$ 6R2 $\qquad$ $44 \div 6 =$ 7R2 $\qquad$ $19 \div 6 =$ 3R1

$90 \div 9 =$ 10 $\qquad$ $52 \div 9 =$ 5R7 $\qquad$ $70 \div 9 =$ 7R7 $\qquad$ $40 \div 9 =$ 4R4

$70 \div 10 =$ 7 $\qquad$ $100 \div 10 =$ 10 $\qquad$ $130 \div 10 =$ 13 $\qquad$ $26 \div 10 =$ 266

$44 \div 11 =$ 4 $\qquad$ $120 \div 11 =$ 12 $\qquad$ $82 \div 11 =$ 7R2 $\qquad$ $211 \div 11 =$

Write the answers.

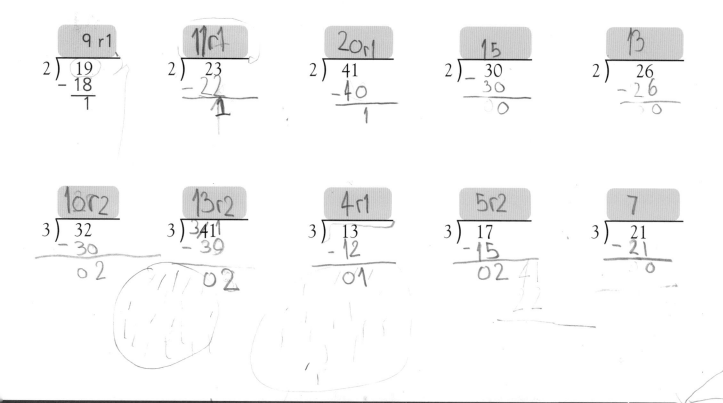

Use the box for your working out.

A packet contains 12 chocolate biscuits. Barbara buys four packets for a party. How many biscuits will Barbara have?

48 biscuits

```
  12
 × 4
 ――
  48
```

Ann runs 800 metres around the school field each day for five days. How far has Ann run in total over the five days?

4000

Songs can be downloaded from a website for 50 p each. Kenny has £1.70 to spend on downloads. How many songs can Kenny download and how much will he have left?

Harris shares 50 bananas equally between 8 monkeys and gives the remainder to a giraffe. How many bananas does the giraffe receive?

r2 bannas

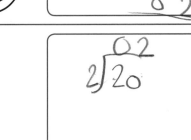

```
   6
 8)50 10
  -48
  ――
   0 2
```

Mark has £20. He shares this with his two sisters and gives the remainder to charity. How much does Mark give to charity?

£2

```
   02
 2)20
```

Children earn £15 a week delivering newspapers. Three children put their weekly earnings together. How much do the children have in total?

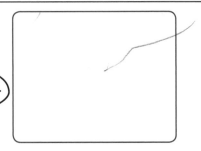

Use the box for your working out.

John earns £12 a week gardening for a neighbour. He works for six weeks. How much has John earned in the six weeks?

£72

```
  12
 ×6
 ──
  72
```

Jo has saved £15 to spend on her holiday. Her holiday will last two weeks. How much will Jo spend each week if she spends the same amount each week?

£210

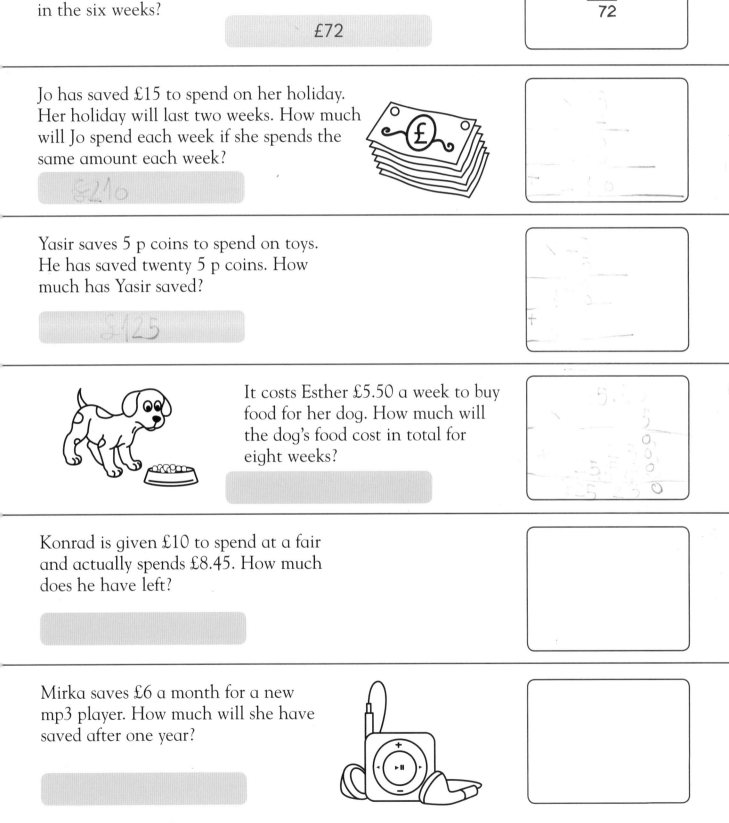

Yasir saves 5 p coins to spend on toys. He has saved twenty 5 p coins. How much has Yasir saved?

£125

It costs Esther £5.50 a week to buy food for her dog. How much will the dog's food cost in total for eight weeks?

Konrad is given £10 to spend at a fair and actually spends £8.45. How much does he have left?

Mirka saves £6 a month for a new mp3 player. How much will she have saved after one year?

Write each length in metres.

8 km	8 000 m	15 km		60 km		100 km	
2.5 km		1.34 km		6.13 km		12.7 km	
7.056 km		1.008 km		5.030 km		8.44 km	

Write each length in centimetres.

2 m		12 m		50 m		9.2 m	
2.1 m		5.5 m		4.85 m		1.94 m	
9.06 m		6.04 m		0.65 m		2.07 m	

Write each weight in grams.

7 kg		18 kg		23 kg		2.1 kg	
8.4 kg		12.7 kg		3.9 kg		5.98 kg	
9.56 kg		2.06 kg		1.08 kg		0.67 kg	

Write each weight in kilograms.

50 g		180 g		4 g		39 g	
546 g		3 005 g		14 000 g		20 000 g	
1 500 g		700 g		7 905 g		3 456 g	

Write each amount in litres.

| 900 ml | | 100 ml | | 2 450 ml | | 4 780 ml | |

Use the box for your working out.

The workmen have laid 562 m of blacktop for a new path. The path has to be 640 m long. How much further do the workmen need to go?

78 m

```
 640
-562
 ───
  78
```

Eleanor has to put 20 litres of orange juice into 40 glasses. How much should Eleanor put in each glass?

Matt needs 380 g of flour for a cake recipe but only has 230 g. How much more flour does Matt need?

Richard has to cut a length of wood to be exactly 53 cm long. He begins with a piece of wood 60 cm long. How much wood does Richard need to cut off?

A large parcel weighs 8 kg. Parcels cost £1.30 per kg to post. How much will the parcel cost to post?

A family travels by car from Cheltenham to Cardiff. The distance between the cities is about 136 km. After 72 km, the car runs out of petrol. How much further is there still to go?

A tortoise can travel 65 cm in 5 minutes. If the tortoise can keep up the same speed, how far will it travel in one hour?

Three children put their money together to buy some flowers.

£2.55   £1.80   £3.20

How much money do they have in total to spend on flowers?

A family drives to Cornwall on holiday. The journey is 285 miles. After 192 miles, they stop for a break. How much further does the family have to travel?

93 miles

$$\begin{array}{r} {}^{1}{}^{1} \\ -2\!\!\!/8\!\!\!/5 \\ 192 \\ \hline 093 \end{array}$$

A teacher gives a test with 25 questions to a class of 9 children. How many questions will the teacher have to mark in total?

In a raffle, only tickets with numbers that were multiples of 9 won a prize. Circle the tickets that won a prize.

Write all the factors of each number.

45

36

A builder puts bricks in piles of 12. A load of 100 bricks is delivered. How many piles will the builder make and how many bricks will be left over?

Complete each problem by filling in the missing operation.

7 ☐ 5 = 35

20 ☐ 4 = 5

16 ☐ 4 = 20

4 ☐ 3 ☐ 2 = 14

10 ☐ 2 ☐ 3 = 8

36 ☐ 4 ☐ 1 = 10

Darius works filling shelves in a supermarket. He is paid £7.85 per hour and works for eight hours a day. How much will Darius earn each day?

£7.85 × 8 =

In a sponsored bike ride, each rider is sponsored £1 per kilometre. These are the distances three riders cycled.

Stefan: 27 km   Jasmine: 23.4 km   Mark: 19.6 km

How much did each rider raise on the cycle ride?

Stefan   Jasmine   Mark

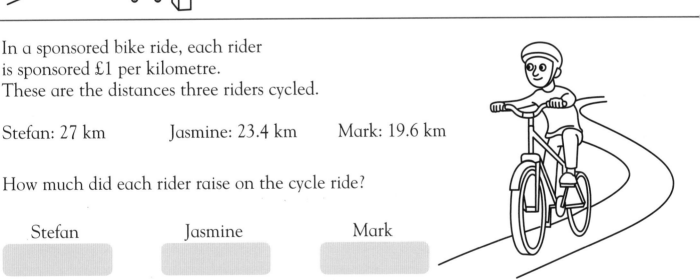

Change each length to millimetres.

3 cm ☐   40 cm ☐   4.2 cm ☐   7.5 cm ☐

Look at this train timetable.

Southport	8.42	9.05	9.14	9.45	10.02	10.24
Westham	9.02	9.25	9.34	10.05	10.22	10.44
Northdon	9.27	9.50	9.59	10.30	10.47	11.09
Eastpool	10.15	10.38	10.47	11.18	11.35	11.57

What time is the first train to leave Southport after 9.00?

9.05

What time does the 9.14 from Southport arrive at Eastpool?

10.47

How long does the journey between Westham and Northdon take?

25 minutes

If the train arrives at Northdon at 10.30, what time did it leave Southport?

How long is the journey from Southport to Eastpool?

If I miss the 9.02 from Westham, how long will I have to wait until the next train?

Which part of the journey between Southport and Eastpool takes 20 minutes?

What time does the train leaving Southport at 10.24 arrive at Northdon?

Darius and Amy go to the cinema to watch a film. The film begins at 7.15 and lasts two and a half hours. What time does the film end?

9.45

It will take a delivery lady 55 minutes to go from the warehouse to a customer. The delivery has to be made by 10.00 a.m. What is the latest time the lady can leave the warehouse?

Each half of a football match lasts 45 minutes. The first half of a match had four minutes added for injuries. The second half had 3 minutes added for injuries. How long was the match in total?

Barbara is going on a fast ferry. The journey takes 4 hours and 20 minutes. If the ferry leaves at 8.30 a.m., what time will it arrive?

Kasim is very fussy about how long to boil his egg. He likes his egg boiled for exactly 210 seconds. How long is 210 seconds in minutes and seconds?

In the morning, Olly wakes up at 8.00 a.m. He spends 8 minutes getting dressed, 20 minutes having breakfast, 5 minutes washing and cleaning his teeth, and is then ready to go to school. At what time is Olly ready to go to school?

An exam is supposed to last one and a half hours but Clara finishes it with 12 minutes to spare. How long does Clara take to complete the exam?

Year 4 children were asked about the foreign language they would like to study.
Look at the bar graph and then answer the questions.

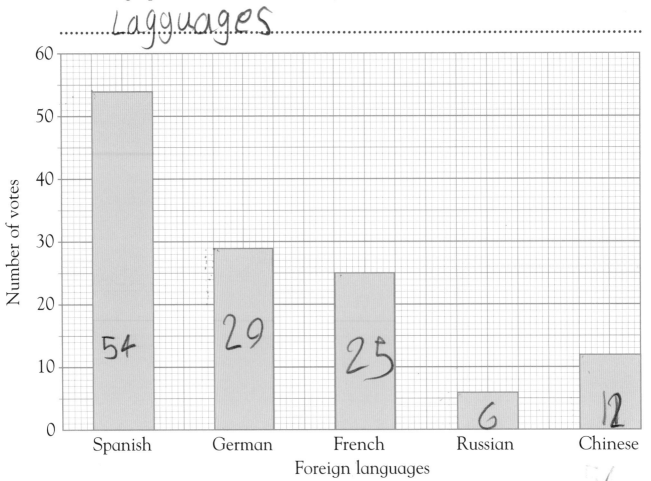

................Lagguages................

The chart does not have a title – write a title for the chart.
Write inside each bar the number of children who voted for the language.

What was the total number of children asked?   126 122

Which languages have less than 20 votes?   Russian, Chinese

Which was the most popular language to learn?   Spanish

Which was the least popular language to learn?   Russian

The school decided not to teach Russian and these
children were taught French instead. How many
children will now study French?   31 6

What is the perimeter of each shape?

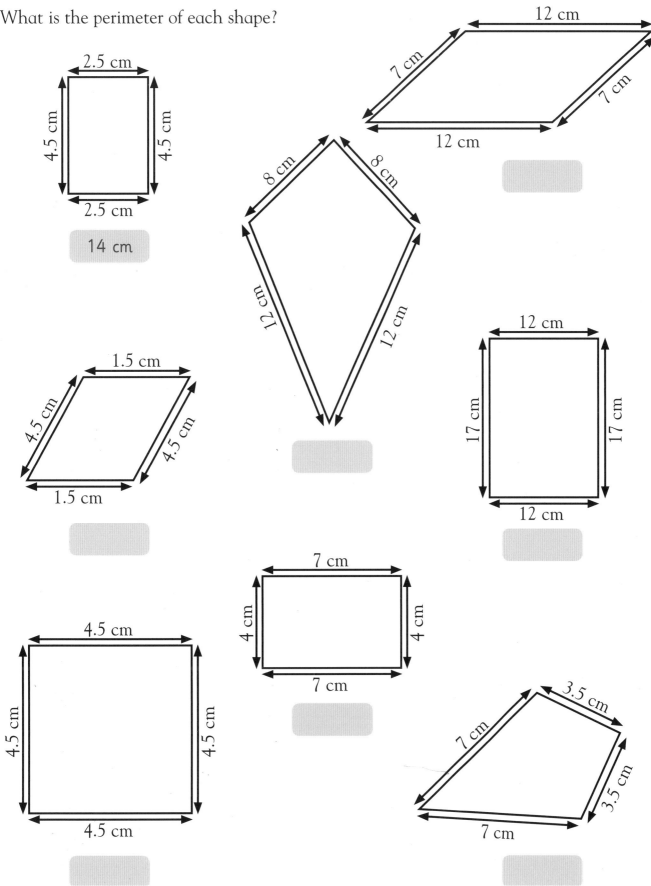

2.5 cm

4.5 cm   4.5 cm

2.5 cm

14 cm

12 cm

7 cm   7 cm

12 cm

8 cm   8 cm

12 cm   12 cm

1.5 cm

4.5 cm   4.5 cm

1.5 cm

12 cm

17 cm   17 cm

12 cm

4.5 cm

4.5 cm   4.5 cm

4.5 cm

7 cm

4 cm   4 cm

7 cm

3.5 cm

7 cm

3.5 cm

7 cm

Use a protractor to carefully measure each angle.

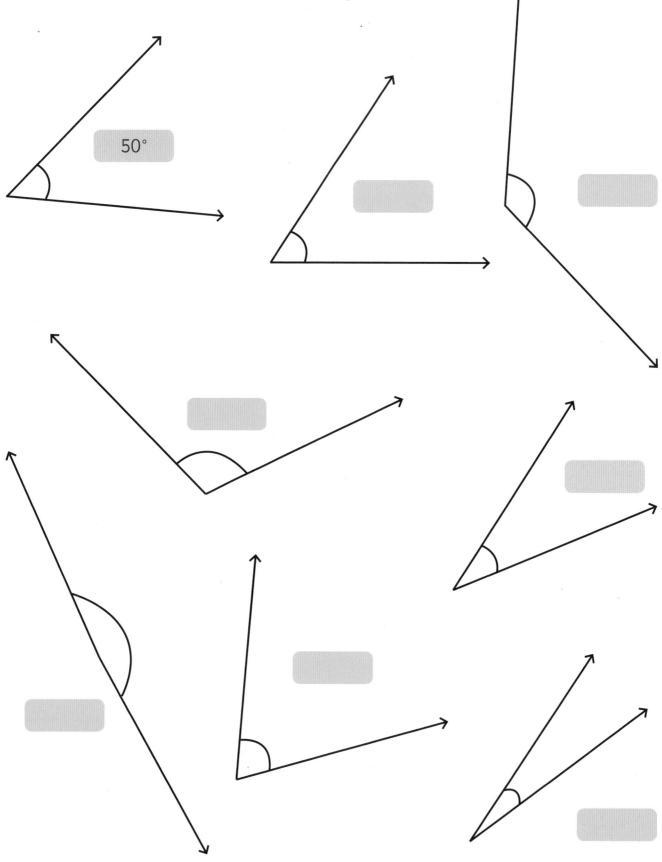

50°

Look at the shapes.

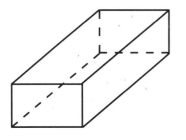

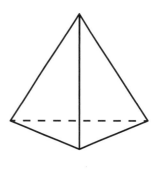

Name of shape ....Cuboid........

Number of faces   6

Number of edges   12

Name of shape ....

Number of faces

Number of edges

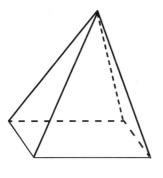

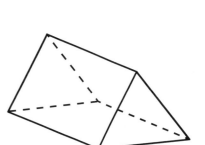

Name of shape ....

Number of faces

Number of edges

Name of shape ....

Number of faces

Number of edges

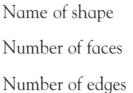

Name of shape ....

Number of faces

Number of edges

Name of shape ....

Number of faces

Number of edges

Use the box for your working out.

Barbara finds out her rail journey will take 3 hours 25 minutes. If Barbara's train journey begins at 9.42 a.m., what time will it end?

A football ground is 95 m long and 75 m across. What is the perimeter of the field?

Ann runs these distances to get fitter.

400 m   600 m   700 m   1 100 m

What is Ann's mean (average) distance?

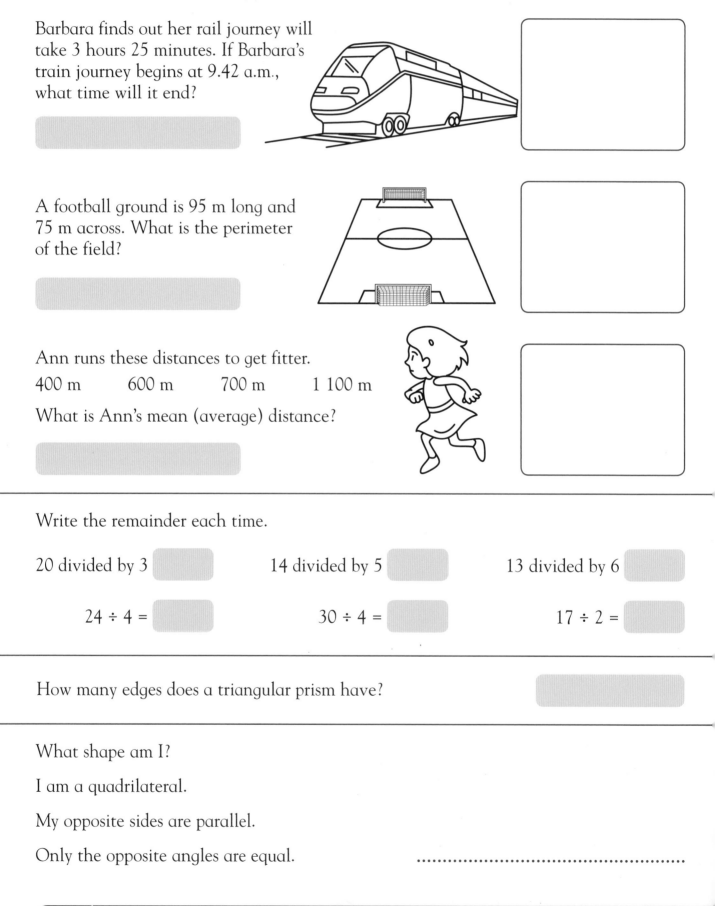

Write the remainder each time.

20 divided by 3 ⬜   14 divided by 5 ⬜   13 divided by 6 ⬜

24 ÷ 4 = ⬜   30 ÷ 4 = ⬜   17 ÷ 2 = ⬜

How many edges does a triangular prism have?   ⬜

What shape am I?

I am a quadrilateral.

My opposite sides are parallel.

Only the opposite angles are equal.   ....

A bricklayer builds a wall around a garden.
This is a plan of the garden.

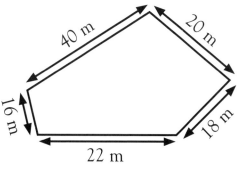

What is the perimeter of the wall that has been built?

A flat piece of rectangular plastic has a square hole cut out.

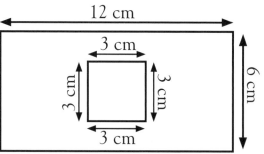

What is the area of the square hole?

What is the area of the rectangle after the square has been removed?

Draw an angle of 65°.

Measure and write down the size of each angle in this triangle.

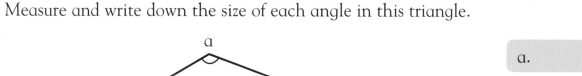

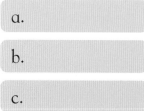

a.

b.

c.

Certificate

Ages
8-9

Congratulations to

....

for successfully
finishing this book.

WELL DONE!

You're a star.

☆ ☆ ☆ ☆ ☆

Date

Answer Section with Parents' Notes

This book helps to support children's understanding of mathematics as they gain familiarity with the concepts of the four operations and they become more proficient and fluent in communicating maths.

Contents
By working through this book, your child will practise:
*   understanding the relative sizes of large numbers;
*   developing fluency with multiplication and division;
*   applying mathematics to solve problems in real-life situations;
*   solving money and time problems;
*   understanding decimal notation for fractions;
*   calculating perimeters of 2-D shapes;
*   classify the properties of 3-D shapes;
*   representing and interpreting data;
*   converting units of measurement;
*   solving problems with units of measurement.

How to help your child
This book provides plenty of practice in solving problems and applying the four operations: +, − , x, and ÷. Children are expected to be able to represent the problems symbolically and communicate the mathematical process clearly. If children really understand the maths, they will be able to reason critically. Do encourage them to explain their reasoning.

Around the home, provide opportunities for practical use of measuring equipment and appropriate tools, such as calculators, watches, timetables, and scales. This will help children to visualise situations when answering maths problems.

Build your child's confidence with words of praise. If they are getting answers wrong, then encourage them to return to try again another time. Good luck and remember to have fun.

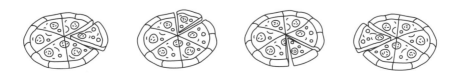

★ Reading and writing numbers

These are large numbers, so be careful how you read and write them.
Write the number in words.

6 124   Six thousand, one hundred and twenty four

5 102   Five thousand, one hundred and two

7 034   Seven thousand and thirty four

11 638   Eleven thousand, six hundred and thirty eight

17 400   Seventeen thousand, four hundred

20 805   Twenty thousand, eight hundred and five

23 967   Twenty-three thousand, nine hundred and sixty seven

97 452   Ninety-seven thousand, four hundred and fifty two

Write the number.

One thousand and forty nine	1 049
Two thousand, nine hundred and eighty four	2 984
Three thousand, four hundred and seventeen	3 417
Six thousand, four hundred and seventy six	6 476
Thirteen thousand, one hundred and six	13 106
Twenty-three thousand and ninety seven	23 097
Sixty thousand and twenty four	60 024
Fifty-four thousand and three	54 003

A single space or a comma is used to separate the thousands and hundreds, and children should be encouraged to use one in that position. Watch out for children mis-reading larger numbers that have a zero somewhere such as 5 102.

Completing sequences ★

Complete each sequence.
Some answers have negative values.

12	24	36	48	60	72	84	96
24	32	40	48	56	64	72	80
18	27	36	45	54	63	72	81
45	50	55	60	65	70	75	80
–40	–35	–30	–25	–20	–15	–10	–5
–18	–15	–12	–9	–6	–3	0	3
–36	–32	–28	–24	–20	–16	–12	–8
–70	–60	–50	–40	–30	–20	–10	0
63	52	41	30	19	8	–3	–14
80	71	62	53	44	35	26	17
26	21	16	11	6	1	–4	–9
–8	–12	–16	–20	–24	–28	–32	–36
13	26	39	52	65	78	91	104
–31	–25	–19	–13	–7	–1	5	11
12	18	24	30	36	42	48	54

Complete this sequence but be careful because this is a bit trickier.

2	4	8	16	32	64	128

Children should begin by looking at the numbers already given and working out the "gaps", after that they should be able to continue the sequences. The sequences with negative numbers will be a little more challenging.

★ Multiplying by 10 and 100

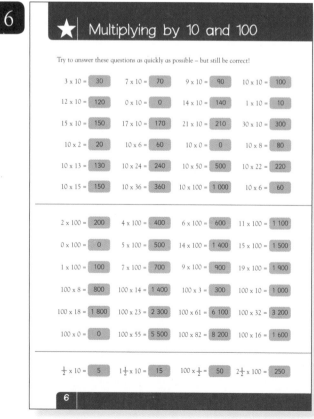

Try to answer these questions as quickly as possible – but still be correct!

3 x 10 = 30	7 x 10 = 70	9 x 10 = 90	10 x 10 = 100
12 x 10 = 120	0 x 10 = 0	14 x 10 = 140	1 x 10 = 10
15 x 10 = 150	17 x 10 = 170	21 x 10 = 210	30 x 10 = 300
10 x 2 = 20	10 x 6 = 60	10 x 0 = 0	10 x 8 = 80
10 x 13 = 130	10 x 24 = 240	10 x 50 = 500	10 x 22 = 220
10 x 15 = 150	10 x 36 = 360	10 x 100 = 1 000	10 x 6 = 60

2 x 100 = 200	4 x 100 = 400	6 x 100 = 600	11 x 100 = 1 100
0 x 100 = 0	5 x 100 = 500	14 x 100 = 1 400	15 x 100 = 1 500
1 x 100 = 100	7 x 100 = 700	9 x 100 = 900	19 x 100 = 1 900
100 x 8 = 800	100 x 14 = 1 400	100 x 3 = 300	100 x 10 = 1 000
100 x 18 = 1 800	100 x 23 = 2 300	100 x 61 = 6 100	100 x 32 = 3 200
100 x 0 = 0	100 x 55 = 5 500	100 x 82 = 8 200	100 x 16 = 1 600

$\frac{1}{2}$ x 10 = 5	$1\frac{1}{2}$ x 10 = 15	100 x $\frac{1}{2}$ = 50	$2\frac{1}{2}$ x 100 = 250

Multiplying whole numbers by 10 and 100 should be learnt by now and will be important when the time comes to move on to multiplying with decimals. Always be careful when multiplying anything by 0 as children sometimes find it hard.

Dividing by 10 and 100 ★

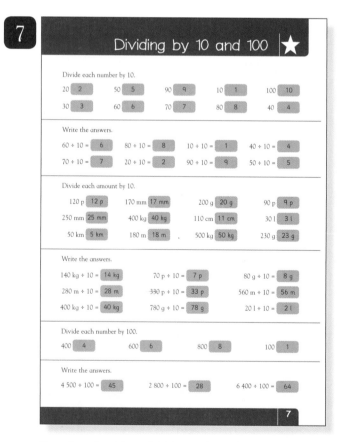

Divide each number by 10.

20 → 2	50 → 5	90 → 9	10 → 1	100 → 10
30 → 3	60 → 6	70 → 7	80 → 8	40 → 4

Write the answers.

60 ÷ 10 = 6	80 ÷ 10 = 8	10 ÷ 10 = 1	40 ÷ 10 = 4
70 ÷ 10 = 7	20 ÷ 10 = 2	90 ÷ 10 = 9	50 ÷ 10 = 5

Divide each amount by 10.

120 p → 12 p	170 mm → 17 mm	200 g → 20 g	90 p → 9 p
250 mm → 25 mm	400 kg → 40 kg	110 cm → 11 cm	30 l → 3 l
50 km → 5 km	180 m → 18 m	500 kg → 50 kg	230 g → 23 g

Write the answers.

140 kg ÷ 10 = 14 kg	70 p ÷ 10 = 7 p	80 g ÷ 10 = 8 g
280 m ÷ 10 = 28 m	330 p ÷ 10 = 33 p	560 m ÷ 10 = 56 m
400 kg ÷ 10 = 40 kg	780 g ÷ 10 = 78 g	20 l ÷ 10 = 2 l

Divide each number by 100.

400 → 4	600 → 6	800 → 8	100 → 1

Write the answers.

4 500 ÷ 100 = 45	2 800 ÷ 100 = 28	6 400 ÷ 100 = 64

Dividing by 10 and 100 can be a little trickier for children although they should be confident when the answers result in whole numbers. Children need to be careful when converting between units such as 3 litres divided by 10.

8

Rounding

Round each amount to the nearest grams (g).

4.6 g	5 g	5.9 g	6 g	4.2 g	4 g	8.5 g	9 g	3.4 g	3 g
0.9 g	1 g	2.7 g	3 g	9.1 g	9 g	5.3 g	5 g	8.8 g	9 g

Round each amount to the nearest centimetre (cm).

12.6 cm	13 cm	14.1 cm	14 cm	13.9 cm	14 cm	18.4 cm	18 cm	15.5 cm	16 cm
21.2 cm	21 cm	26.8 cm	27 cm	19.3 cm	19 cm	23.7 cm	24 cm	16.5 cm	17 cm

Round each amount to the nearest pound (£).

£1.12	£1	£3.50	£4	£2.78	£3	£4.90	£5	£1.35	£1
£4.66	£5	£8.85	£9	£3.27	£3	£0.70	£1	£7.51	£8
£12.06	£12	£6.50	£7	£1.80	£2	£2.63	£3	£5.05	£5

Round each amount to the nearest kilograms (kg).

0.85 kg	1 kg	1.34 kg	1 kg	2.51 kg	3 kg	2.02 kg	2 kg	1.05 kg	1 kg
3.56 kg	4 kg	2.75 kg	3 kg	4.19 kg	4 kg	2.38 kg	2 kg	4.52 kg	5 kg

Round each number to the nearest whole number.

6.4	6	8.3	8	12.1	12	8.2	8	4.9	5
6.5	7	11.7	12	3.6	4	8.8	9	10.5	11
3.45	3	2.06	2	3.01	3	4.08	4	5.09	5

8

At this stage, rounding should be fairly straightforward as long as children remember the rule about the "half position" being rounded upwards, such as 6.5 becoming 7.

9

Comparing numbers

Circle the larger number or amount each time.

0.5 or 0.3	0.5 kg or **600 g**	**$\frac{1}{2}$** or 0.3
1.2 or **2.1**	**70 cm** or 0.5 m	**£2.40** or 189 p
5.6 m or **600 cm**	0.3 or **0.4**	£1.90 or **£5.00**

Circle the smaller number or amount each time.

0.8 or **$\frac{1}{2}$**	3.5 m or **290 mm**	4.2 or **2.4**
3.5 or 5.3	625 cm or **6.2 m**	**130 g** or 1.2 kg
3.5 l or **$3\frac{1}{3}$ l**	£3.50 or **250 p**	**65 cm** or 1 m

Circle the larger number or amount each time.

6 x 7 or 40	**2 x 12** or 22	**double 150** or 295
3.5 km or half of 5 km	**3 x 8** or 6 x 3	£2.50 or **300 p**
400 ml or **0.5 l**	**40 x 2** or 10 x 7	**4 m** or 54 cm

Circle the smaller number or amount each time.

6 kg or **53 g**	6.72 or **6.27**	**£7.00** or 1000 p
12 km or **half of 14 km**	**4.01** or 4.1	2 km or **1 600 m**
2.65 km or **2.56 km**	**4.2 g** or 0.5 kg	**3.6 m** or 400 cm

Circle the larger number each time.

10 x 11 or **12 x 10**	**8 x 7** or 6 x 9	7 x 4 or **6 x 5**
4 x 11 or 6 x 7	6 x 4 or **9 x 3**	11 x 3 or **9 x 8**
5 x 8 or 7 x 5	**6 x 6** or 8 x 4	**10 x 5** or 5 x 5

9

Much of this work revolves around children being able to successfully change between units. Understanding that in order to find some answers, information such as "there are 100 cm in a metre" will be essential.

10

Fractions

What is half ($\frac{1}{2}$) of each amount?

£3.00	£1.50	£5.00	£2.50	6 kg	3 kg	3 g	1.5 g	60 m	30 m
£1.20	£0.60	£1.50	£0.75	12 ml	6 ml	£2.50	£1.25	6 m	3 m

What is two-thirds ($\frac{2}{3}$) of each amount?

12 m	8 m	21 kg	14 kg	15 g	10 g	£6.00	£4.00	30 m	20 m
18 g	12 g	£3.00	£2.00	21 km	14 km	24 kg	16 kg	15 m	10 m

What is a quarter ($\frac{1}{4}$) of each amount?

£1.00	£0.25	60 cm	15 cm	2 m	0.5 m	48 g	12 g	£4.00	£1.00
120 cm	30 cm	80 g	20 g	12 kg	3 kg	32 p	8 p	56 g	14 g

What is one-fifth ($\frac{1}{5}$) of each amount?

20 p	4 p	50 p	10 p	10 p	2 p	25 cm	5 cm	£20.00	£4.00
60 cm	12 cm	10 m	2 m	40 km	8 km	35 g	7 g	45 kg	9 kg

What is two-fifths ($\frac{2}{5}$) of each amount?

30 p	12 p	£20.00	£8.00	10 cm	4 cm	5 m	2 m	2 m	80 cm
40 p	16 p	50 g	20 g	60 kg	24 kg	55 p	22 p	25 p	10 p

10

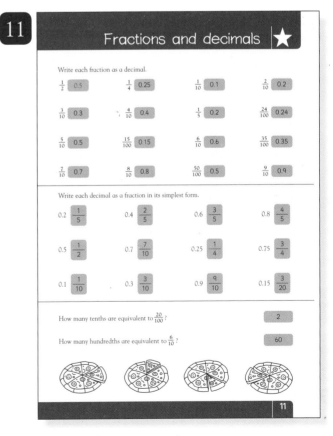

By now children should be familiar with the common fractions such as $\frac{1}{2}$, $\frac{1}{4}$, and $\frac{3}{4}$. Fifths and tenths will be less familiar but will become so. With fractions such as $\frac{2}{3}$, encourage children to first work out $\frac{1}{3}$ and then double the number.

11

Fractions and decimals

Write each fraction as a decimal.

$\frac{1}{2}$	0.5	$\frac{1}{4}$	0.25	$\frac{1}{10}$	0.1	$\frac{2}{10}$	0.2
$\frac{3}{10}$	0.3	$\frac{4}{10}$	0.4	$\frac{1}{5}$	0.2	$\frac{24}{100}$	0.24
$\frac{5}{10}$	0.5	$\frac{15}{100}$	0.15	$\frac{6}{10}$	0.6	$\frac{35}{100}$	0.35
$\frac{7}{10}$	0.7	$\frac{8}{10}$	0.8	$\frac{50}{100}$	0.5	$\frac{9}{10}$	0.9

Write each decimal as a fraction in its simplest form.

0.2	$\frac{1}{5}$	0.4	$\frac{2}{5}$	0.6	$\frac{3}{5}$	0.8	$\frac{4}{5}$
0.5	$\frac{1}{2}$	0.7	$\frac{7}{10}$	0.25	$\frac{1}{4}$	0.75	$\frac{3}{4}$
0.1	$\frac{1}{10}$	0.3	$\frac{3}{10}$	0.9	$\frac{9}{10}$	0.15	$\frac{3}{20}$

How many tenths are equivalent to $\frac{20}{100}$? 2

How many hundredths are equivalent to $\frac{6}{10}$? 60

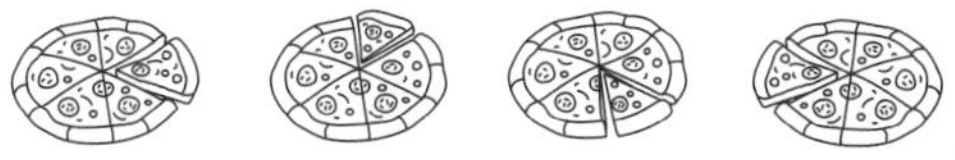

11

Children should know the connection between fractions and decimals and be able to interchange them with ease, especially tenths and hundredths. Note that they may not have been formally taught this conversion.

★ Keeping skills sharp

Which of these is the same as 20 305? Circle the correct answer.

Twenty thousand, three hundred and fifty   Twenty-three thousand and five

(Twenty thousand, three hundred and five)   Twenty thousand and thirty five

Complete each sequence.

18	14	10	6	2	–2	–6	–10

–14	–9	–4	1	6	11	16	21

12	10	8	6	4	2	0	–2

Write the answers.

45 × 10	100 × 27	100 × 0.5	78 × 100
450	2 700	50	7 800

Find the answer to each problem.

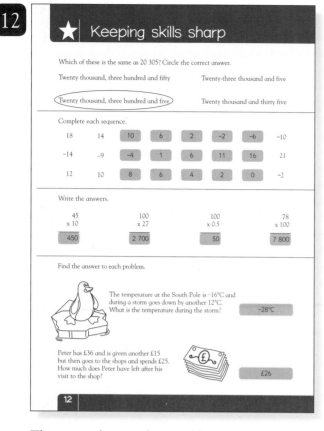

The temperature at the South Pole is –16°C and during a storm goes down by another 12°C. What is the temperature during the storm?   **–28°C**

Peter has £36 and is given another £15 but then goes to the shops and spends £25. How much does Peter have left after his visit to the shop?   **£26**

Keeping skills sharp ★

Place the amounts in order, starting with the smallest.

£6.50	560 p	£6.05	£65.00	680 p	£5.06
£5.06	560 p	£6.05	£6.50	680 p	£65.00

These are some of the ingredients for a cake.

Round each amount to the nearest 10 g.

6 g of salt   _10 g of salt_

122 g of flour   _120 g of flour_

67 g of cherries   _70 g of cherries_

45 g of almonds   _50 g of almonds_

A class usually has 33 children but two-thirds are away on a trip. How many children did not go on the trip?   **11**

How many tenths are equivalent to one half?   **5**

How many thirds are equivalent to one whole?   **3**

How many quarters are equivalent to 2?   **8**

Write each decimal as a fraction.

$0.5 \quad \frac{1}{2}$ $0.2 \quad \frac{2}{10}$ $0.75 \quad \frac{3}{4}$ $0.9 \quad \frac{9}{10}$

Write each fraction as a decimal.

$\frac{4}{10} \quad 0.4$ $\frac{7}{10} \quad 0.7$ $\frac{37}{100} \quad 0.37$ $\frac{12}{100} \quad 0.12$

This page along with page 13 acts as revision and a reminder of the work in the previous pages. It can be given as a test if required.

★ Adding

Write the answers.

46 + 20 = **66**	21 + 30 = **51**	54 + 40 = **94**	53 + 10 = **63**
73 + 30 = **103**	69 + 40 = **109**	45 + 70 = **115**	95 + 20 = **115**
67 + 50 = **117**	70 + 60 = **130**	90 + 90 = **180**	40 + 80 = **120**
49 + 13 = **62**	52 + 18 = **70**	62 + 12 = **74**	37 + 16 = **53**
46 + 32 = **78**	53 + 27 = **80**	38 + 43 = **81**	74 + 17 = **91**
76 + 28 = **104**	44 + 66 = **110**	12 + 73 = **85**	55 + 23 = **78**

Write the answers.

73 + 15	56 + 17	39 + 24	52 + 38	51 + 26
88	**73**	**63**	**90**	**77**

25 + 45	67 + 44	48 + 28	90 + 23	85 + 17
70	**111**	**76**	**113**	**102**

Write the answers.

£8 + £80 + £4 = **£92**   £45 + £25 + £15 = **£85**

60 cm + 6 cm + 12 cm = **78 cm**   12 p + 24 p + 36 p = **72 p**

32 cm + 64 cm + 8 cm = **104 cm**   35 p + 45 p + 16 p = **96 p**

21 cm + 20 cm + 19 cm = **60 cm**   12 p + 13 p + 14 p = **39 p**

Children should have methods of solving addition problems in both their vertical and horizontal forms. As children become more proficient at maths, they should see the importance of reaching the answer speedily.

Subtracting ★

Write the answers.

40 – 12 = **28**	50 – 17 = **33**	60 – 11 = **49**	80 – 19 = **61**
90 – 18 = **72**	30 – 10 = **20**	100 – 15 = **85**	60 – 45 = **15**
26 – 14 = **12**	39 – 16 = **23**	42 – 11 = **31**	63 – 22 = **41**
76 – 34 = **42**	96 – 45 = **51**	54 – 40 = **14**	59 – 28 = **31**
46 – 17 = **29**	52 – 16 = **36**	73 – 19 = **54**	25 – 17 = **8**
34 – 18 = **16**	48 – 29 = **19**	40 – 26 = **14**	81 – 44 = **37**

Write the answers.

35 – 12	41 – 20	57 – 25	63 – 41	44 – 34
23	**21**	**32**	**22**	**10**

27 – 19	32 – 14	54 – 26	70 – 37	36 – 17
8	**18**	**28**	**33**	**19**

Write the answers.

47 cm – 34 cm = **13 cm**   59 p – 28 p = **31 p**   70 m – 32 m = **38 m**

£40 – £26 = **£14**   61 p – 34 p = **27 p**   73 cm – 48 cm = **25 cm**

64 m – 49 m = **15 m**   53 p – 49 p = **4 p**   25 p – 24 p = **1 p**

21 p – 17 p = **4 p**   41 p – 38 p = **3 p**   £98 – £45 = **£53**

As with addition on the previous page, children should by now be able to work out these sums both quickly and accurately.

Multiplying

Write the answers.

$35 \times 3 = 105$ $42 \times 3 = 126$ $38 \times 5 = 190$ $74 \times 3 = 222$

$69 \times 2 = 138$ $71 \times 3 = 213$ $56 \times 4 = 224$ $73 \times 3 = 219$

$67 \times 4 = 268$ $58 \times 2 = 116$ $14 \times 6 = 84$ $23 \times 6 = 138$

$44 \times 3 = 132$ $52 \times 6 = 312$ $46 \times 3 = 138$ $32 \times 4 = 128$

Write the answers.

29×3	36×4	45×5	54×6	62×7
87	144	225	324	434

71×4	86×3	93×4	73×5	64×2
284	258	372	365	128

59×4	43×5	23×6	38×4	40×6
236	215	138	152	240

56×3	63×4	76×2	41×5	67×7
168	252	152	205	469

78×8	89×10	37×5	48×6	59×7
624	890	185	288	413

Most schools will teach multiplication in both horizontal and vertical forms and children should have been given strategies to work sums in different ways.

Dividing with remainders

Write the answers. Some of these answers may have remainders.

$27 \div 4 = 6\ r3$ $24 \div 4 = 6$ $47 \div 4 = 11\ r3$ $44 \div 4 = 11$

$29 \div 3 = 9\ r2$ $14 \div 3 = 4\ r2$ $17 \div 3 = 5\ r2$ $21 \div 3 = 7$

$12 \div 7 = 1\ r5$ $56 \div 7 = 8$ $77 \div 7 = 11$ $23 \div 7 = 3\ r2$

$15 \div 5 = 3$ $6 \div 5 = 1\ r1$ $12 \div 5 = 2\ r2$ $34 \div 5 = 6\ r4$

$10 \div 8 = 1\ r2$ $57 \div 8 = 7\ r1$ $84 \div 8 = 10\ r4$ $24 \div 8 = 3$

$48 \div 6 = 8$ $38 \div 6 = 6\ r2$ $44 \div 6 = 7\ r2$ $19 \div 6 = 3\ r1$

$90 \div 9 = 10$ $52 \div 9 = 5\ r7$ $70 \div 9 = 7\ r7$ $40 \div 9 = 4\ r4$

$70 \div 10 = 7$ $100 \div 10 = 10$ $130 \div 10 = 13$ $26 \div 10 = 2\ r6$

$44 \div 11 = 4$ $120 \div 11 = 10\ r10$ $82 \div 11 = 7\ r5$ $211 \div 11 = 19\ r2$

Write the answers.

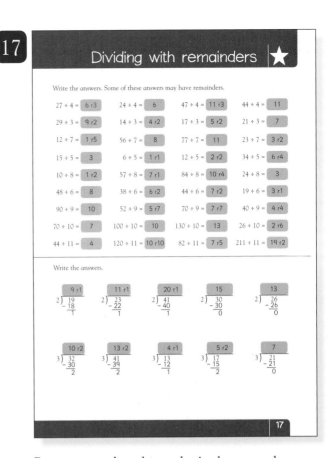

9 r1	11 r1	20 r1	15	13
2)19 −18 = 1	2)23 −22 = 1	2)41 −40 = 1	2)30 −30 = 0	2)26 −26 = 0

10 r2	13 r2	4 r1	5 r2	7
3)32 −30 = 2	3)41 −39 = 2	3)13 −12 = 1	3)17 −15 = 2	3)21 −21 = 0

Recognising that things don't always work out exactly is interesting for children. Division with remainders is an example. Children may have been shown various ways to write down the calculation but it is usual for an "r" to be used.

Real-life problems

Use the box for your working out.

A packet contains 12 chocolate biscuits. Barbara buys four packets for a party. How many biscuits will Barbara have?

$\begin{array}{r} 12 \\ \times\ 4 \\ \hline 48 \end{array}$

48 biscuits

Ann runs 800 metres around the school field each day for five days. How far has Ann run in total over the five days?

4 000 metres

Songs can be downloaded from a website for 50 p each. Kenny has £1.70 to spend on downloads. How many songs can Kenny download and how much will he have left?

3 songs and 20 p left

Harris shares 50 bananas equally between 8 monkeys and gives the remainder to a giraffe. How many bananas does the giraffe receive?

2 bananas

Mark has £20. He shares this with his two sisters and gives the remainder to charity. How much does Mark give to charity?

£2

Children earn £15 a week delivering newspapers. Three children put their weekly earnings together. How much do the children have in total?

£45

Once again, children will need to have the ability to sort out "what needs to be done". When a strategy has been developed, the next step is to carefully, quickly, and accurately work out the answer.

Money problems

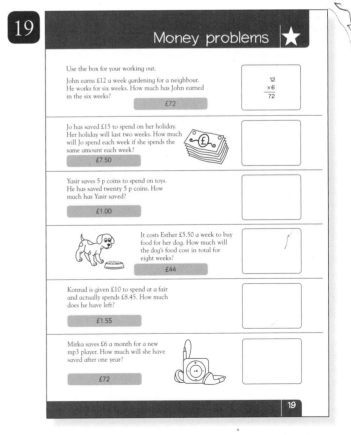

Use the box for your working out.

John earns £12 a week gardening for a neighbour. He works for six weeks. How much has John earned in the six weeks?

$\begin{array}{r} 12 \\ \times\ 6 \\ \hline 72 \end{array}$

£72

Jo has saved £15 to spend on her holiday. Her holiday will last two weeks. How much will Jo spend each week if she spends the same amount each week?

£7.50

Yasir saves 5 p coins to spend on toys. He has saved twenty 5 p coins. How much has Yasir saved?

£1.00

It costs Esther £5.50 a week to buy food for her dog. How much will the dog's food cost in total for eight weeks?

£44

Konrad is given £10 to spend at a fair and actually spends £8.45. How much does he have left?

£1.55

Mirka saves £6 a month for a new mp3 player. How much will she have saved after one year?

£72

Children should be able to see fairly easily what is required by way of working out and then carry out the problem quickly and accurately.

★ Units of measurement

Write each length in metres.

8 km `8 000 m`	15 km `15 000 m`	60 km `60 000 m`	100 km `100 000 m`
2.5 km `2 500 m`	1.34 km `1 340 m`	6.13 km `6 130 m`	12.7 km `12 700 m`
7.056 km `7 056 m`	1.008 km `1 008 m`	5.030 km `5 030 m`	8.44 km `8 440 m`

Write each length in centimetres.

2 m `200 cm`	12 m `1 200 cm`	50 m `5 000 cm`	9.2 m `920 cm`
2.1 m `210 cm`	5.5 m `550 cm`	4.85 m `485 cm`	1.94 m `194 cm`
9.06 m `906 cm`	6.04 m `604 cm`	0.65 m `65 cm`	2.07 m `207 cm`

Write each weight in grams.

7 kg `7 000 g`	18 kg `18 000 g`	23 kg `23 000 g`	2.1 kg `2 100 g`
8.4 kg `8 400 g`	12.7 kg `12 700 g`	3.9 kg `3 900 g`	5.98 kg `5 980 g`
9.56 kg `9 560 g`	2.06 kg `2 060 g`	1.08 kg `1 080 g`	0.67 kg `670 g`

Write each weight in kilograms.

50 g `0.05 kg`	180 g `0.180 kg`	4 g `0.004 kg`	39 g `0.039 kg`
546 g `0.546 kg`	3 005 g `3.005 kg`	14 000 g `14 kg`	20 000 g `20 kg`
1 500 g `1.5 kg`	700 g `0.7 kg`	7 905 g `7.905 kg`	3 456 g `3.456 kg`

Write each amount in litres.

900 ml `0.9 l`	100 ml `0.1 l`	2 450 ml `2.45 l`	4 780 ml `4.78 l`

Most units are not commonly or often used in everyday life so children do not have many opportunities to be reminded about them. The metric units of measurements are important and children should be given practice on them.

Measuring problems ★

Use the box for your working out.
The workmen have laid 562 m of blacktop for a new path. The path has to be 640 m long. How much further do the workmen need to go? `78 m`

```
  640
- 562
  ----
   78
```

Eleanor has to put 20 litres of orange juice into 40 glasses. How much should Eleanor put in each glass? `half a litre`

Matt needs 380 g of flour for a cake recipe but only has 230 g. How much more flour does Matt need? `150 g`

Richard has to cut a length of wood to be exactly 53 cm long. He begins with a piece of wood 60 cm long. How much wood does Richard need to cut off? `7 cm`

A large parcel weighs 8 kg. Parcels cost £1.30 per kg to post. How much will the parcel cost to post? `£10.40`

A family travels by car from Cheltenham to Cardiff. The distance between the cities is about 136 km. After 72 km, the car runs out of petrol. How much further is there still to go? `64 km`

A tortoise can travel 65 cm in 5 minutes. If the tortoise can keep up the same speed, how far will it travel in one hour? `780 cm`

These questions give more practice in deciding which operation is needed. As children grow older, more and more maths will depend upon them being able to "see the problem" and then use the best method to solve it.

★ Keeping skills sharp

Three children put their money together to buy some flowers.

£2.55   £1.80   £3.20

How much money do they have in total to spend on flowers? `£7.55`

A family drives to Cornwall on holiday. The journey is 285 miles. After 192 miles, they stop for a break. How much further does the family have to travel? `93 miles`

A teacher gives a test with 25 questions to a class of 9 children. How many questions will the teacher have to mark in total? `225`

In a raffle, only tickets with numbers that were multiples of 9 won a prize. Circle the tickets that won a prize.

12   57   (180)   (27)   100
(15)   13   (24)
(96)   (90)   (18)   44

Write all the factors of each number.

45 `1, 3, 5, 9, 15, and 45`   36 `1, 2, 3, 4, 6, 9, 12, 18, and 36`

This test reinforces the skills learned so far. It can be repeated as often as appropriate but should be used mainly to highlight areas where children are doing well and those where further practice is necessary.

Keeping skills sharp ★

A builder puts bricks in piles of 12. A load of 100 bricks is delivered. How many piles will the builder make and how many bricks will be left over? `8 piles and 4 left over`

Complete each problem by filling in the missing operation.

7 `x` 5 = 35   20 `÷` 4 = 5   16 `+` 4 = 20

4 `x` 3 `+` 2 = 14   10 `+` 2 `+` 3 = 8   36 `÷` 4 `+` 1 = 10

Darius works filling shelves in a supermarket. He is paid £7.85 per hour and works for eight hours a day. How much will Darius earn each day? `£62.80`

In a sponsored bike ride, each rider is sponsored £1 per kilometre. These are the distances three riders cycled.

Stefan: 27 km   Jasmine: 23.4 km   Mark: 19.6 km

How much did each rider raise on the cycle ride?

Stefan	Jasmine	Mark
`£27`	`£23.40`	`£19.60`

Change each length to millimetres.

3 cm `30 mm`   40 cm `400 mm`   4.2 cm `42 mm`   7.5 cm `75 mm`

★ Reading timetables

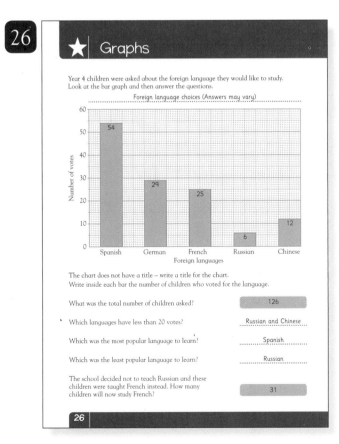

Look at this train timetable.

Southport	8.42	9.05	9.14	9.45	10.02	10.24
Westham	9.02	9.25	9.34	10.05	10.22	10.44
Northdon	9.27	9.50	9.59	10.30	10.47	11.09
Eastpool	10.15	10.38	10.47	11.18	11.35	11.57

What time is the first train to leave Southport after 9.00? **9.05**

What time does the 9.14 from Southport arrive at Eastpool? **10.47**

How long does the journey between Westham and Northdon take? **25 minutes**

If the train arrives at Northdon at 10.30, what time did it leave Southport? **9.45**

How long is the journey from Southport to Eastpool? **1 hour and 33 minutes**

If I miss the 9.02 from Westham, how long will I have to wait until the next train? **23 minutes**

Which part of the journey between Southport and Eastpool takes 20 minutes? **Southport to Westham**

What time does the train leaving Southport at 10.24 arrive at Northdon? **11.09**

Children see many timetables as they grow up from TV menus of programmes to film times. The skills are usually straightforward but the more practice the better.

Time problems ★

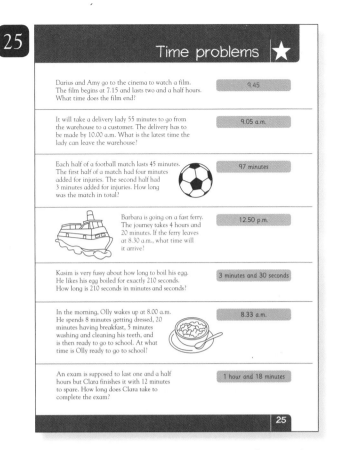

Darius and Amy go to the cinema to watch a film. The film begins at 7.15 and lasts two and a half hours. What time does the film end? **9.45**

It will take a delivery lady 55 minutes to go from the warehouse to a customer. The delivery has to be made by 10.00 a.m. What is the latest time the lady can leave the warehouse? **9.05 a.m.**

Each half of a football match lasts 45 minutes. The first half of a match had four minutes added for injuries. The second half had 3 minutes added for injuries. How long was the match in total? **97 minutes**

Barbara is going on a fast ferry. The journey takes 4 hours and 20 minutes. If the ferry leaves at 8.30 a.m., what time will it arrive? **12.50 p.m.**

Kasim is very fussy about how long to boil his egg. He likes his egg boiled for exactly 210 seconds. How long is 210 seconds in minutes and seconds? **3 minutes and 30 seconds**

In the morning, Olly wakes up at 8.00 a.m. He spends 8 minutes getting dressed, 20 minutes having breakfast, 5 minutes washing and cleaning his teeth, and is then ready to go to school. At what time is Olly ready to go to school? **8.33 a.m.**

An exam is supposed to last one and a half hours but Clara finishes it with 12 minutes to spare. How long does Clara take to complete the exam? **1 hour and 18 minutes**

By now, children should be very confident with using various clock types to tell the time but may need practice in working with time, such as finding out "how much longer?" or "when will we arrive?".

★ Graphs

Year 4 children were asked about the foreign language they would like to study. Look at the bar graph and then answer the questions.

Foreign language choices (Answers may vary)

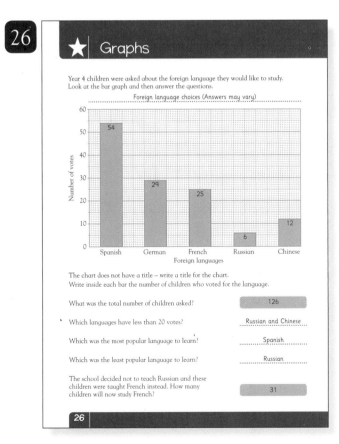

The chart does not have a title – write a title for the chart.
Write inside each bar the number of children who voted for the language.

What was the total number of children asked? **126**

Which languages have less than 20 votes? Russian and Chinese

Which was the most popular language to learn? Spanish

Which was the least popular language to learn? Russian

The school decided not to teach Russian and these children were taught French instead. How many children will now study French? **31**

Children will know that it is good practice to label a graph with a title and a heading for the two axis. The chosen title may vary from the suggestion above.

Perimeters ★

What is the perimeter of each shape?

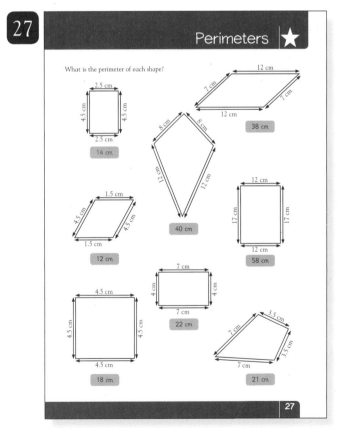

Children are usually taught that "perimeter is the distance around the outside of a shape" and should cope well as long as they add carefully.

★ Angles

Use a protractor to carefully measure each angle.

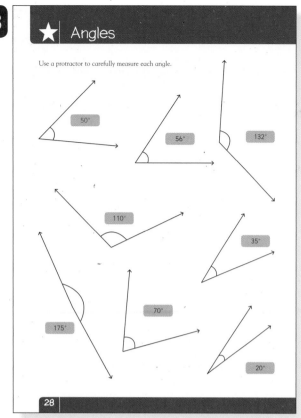

50°
56°
132°
110°
35°
175°
70°
20°

Protractors can vary in design – the traditional ones will have two possibilities for an "answer". Ask children to measure carefully and also tell you whether the angle is acute, right, or obtuse. Check their familiarity with these terms.

Properties of 3-D shapes ★

Look at the shapes.

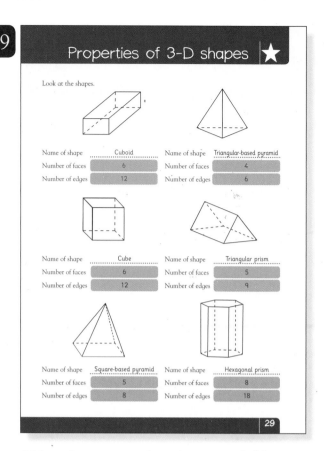

Name of shape	Cuboid	Name of shape	Triangular-based pyramid
Number of faces	6	Number of faces	4
Number of edges	12	Number of edges	6

Name of shape	Cube	Name of shape	Triangular prism
Number of faces	6	Number of faces	5
Number of edges	12	Number of edges	9

Name of shape	Square-based pyramid	Name of shape	Hexagonal prism
Number of faces	5	Number of faces	8
Number of edges	8	Number of edges	18

Although not covered on this page, children should know that faces can be flat or curved and that an edge happens when two faces meet.

★ Keeping skills sharp

Use the box for your working out.

Barbara finds out her rail journey will take 3 hours 25 minutes. If Barbara's train journey begins at 9.42 a.m., what time will it end?

1.07 p.m.

A football ground is 95 m long and 75 m across. What is the perimeter of the field?

340 m

Ann runs these distances to get fitter.
400 m   600 m   700 m   1 100 m
What is Ann's mean (average) distance?

700 m

Write the remainder each time.

20 divided by 3 2   14 divided by 5 4   13 divided by 6 1

24 ÷ 4 = 0   30 ÷ 4 = 2   17 ÷ 2 = 1

How many edges does a triangular prism have?   9

What shape am I?
I am a quadrilateral.
My opposite sides are parallel.
Only the opposite angles are equal.   .... Parallelogram

The final two pages are an additional test that children can use to find out how well they have understood the work so far.

Keeping skills sharp ★

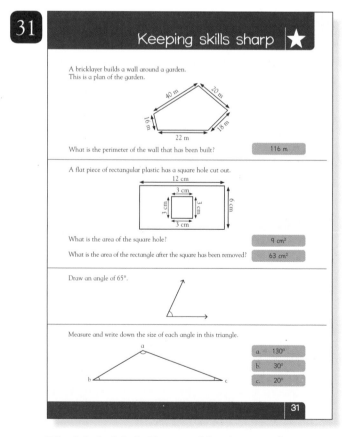

A bricklayer builds a wall around a garden. This is a plan of the garden.

40 m   20 m   16 m   18 m   22 m

What is the perimeter of the wall that has been built?   116 m

A flat piece of rectangular plastic has a square hole cut out.

12 cm   3 cm   3 cm   3 cm   3 cm   6 cm

What is the area of the square hole?   9 cm²

What is the area of the rectangle after the square has been removed?   63 cm²

Draw an angle of 65°.

Measure and write down the size of each angle in this triangle.

a
b   c

a.   130°
b.   30°
c.   20°

The *Maths Made Easy* workbooks provide more practice pages.